TALES TO TELL

Written and Illustrated by:

JAMES HAROLD GAGE Sr.

Short stories suited to help English
students master basic reading skills

TALES TO TELL

Written and Illustrated by:
JAMES HAROLD GAGE Sr.

Digital Graphics and Watercolor
by Tiffany Jones

ISBN 978-1-947598-16-4 Paperback
Copyright © 2021 by James H. Gage

Published by:
BOOGIE BOOKHOUSE

A Division of:
BAPTIST TRAINING CENTER PUBLICATIONS

Winter Haven, Florida

DEDICATION

I dedicate this book to my grandkids: Frank and Beenne Anglin, Kirsten, Karissa, and Nathanael Allen, Forest and Dusty Gage, Santiago Gonzalez, and Joshua Bernal. I also dedicate this book to the many English students throughout the years that have been my joy to teach.

PREFACE

These short stories are written to help students master necessary reading skills. The drawings are mental storyboards helping students navigate new thought processes in English. Written as short bedtime stories, they provide moral insights on education, motivation, inspiration, love, and family. May the reader enjoy these learning adventures.

TABLE OF CONTENTS

CHAPTER ONE

HOW TO GET RID OF A DEAD DOG

Mary was an old widow who lived alone in an apartment building. She was poor and did not have any friends. There were no relatives that lived nearby. All she had was her trusty dog, her faithful friend Rover. She took care of her friend. "I love you, Rover; you are my faithful friend. You are my only friend," she whispered in Rover's ear.

But one day, Rover got sick. The old widow lady did everything she could to help Rover recover. Mary tried to make him as comfortable as possible by placing him close to the fireplace and giving him food to eat. But nothing she did helped Rover. When all efforts had failed, Rover died. It was a sad day for Mary, the old widow.

ONE DAY, ROVER GOT SICK. SHE DID EVERYTHING POSSIBLE TO SAVE ROVER, BUT ROVER DIED!

OH! WHAT AM I GOING TO DO?

HOW CAN I GET RID OF ROVER? THERE IS NO PLACE TO BURY ROVER.

It was a big problem. "What am I going to do? How can I get rid of Rover? There is no place to bury Rover in the apartment building," she thought to herself. She had no one to call to help her. It was a huge problem.

Finally, she called the dog pound. They said, "bring us the dead dog. We will take care of the problem."

But now, she had another problem. How do I get dead Rover to the dog pound? Rover was big and weighed quite a lot. She didn't have a car, nor any money to take a taxi. There were no friends that could help. Nor did she have any family that lived nearby. It was a big dilemma for the old widow. She sat down in her rocking chair and thought, "What am I going to do?"

SHE CALLED THE DOG POUND.

THEY SAID, "BRING US THE DEAD DOG. WE WILL TAKE CARE OF THE PROBLEM."

DOG POUND

And then she came up with an idea. She went to the closet and took out an old suitcase. Then she opened the lid, picked up Rover, and put him inside. Then the old widow took the luggage to the bus stop. It was heavy and cumbersome, but she managed to get there.

At the bus stop, there was a man. "May I help you with your suitcase?" asked the man.

"Oh, thank you. You are such a nice man," said the old widow.

WHEN THE BUS ARRIVED, HE PICKED UP THE SUITCASE. THEN, THEY GOT ON THE BUS. HE PUT THE SUITCASE DOWN BESIDE THE WOMAN, THEN HE SAT DOWN BEHIND HER.

THE MAN BEGAN TO THINK THAT THE SUITCASE WAS VERY HEAVY. "I'LL BET SHE HAS SOMETHING VALUABLE IN IT."

SO AT THE NEXT BUS STOP, THE MAN GRABBED THE SUITCASE.

THE MAN SAT DOWN BEHIND THE WOMAN.

THE WIDOW SAT DOWN IN FRONT OF THE MAN.

BUS STOP

HE RAN OUT OF THE BUS AND DOWN THE STREET.

THEY GOT ON THE BUS.

The two sat down on the bench at the bus stop to wait for the bus. Soon the bus arrived. The old widow got on the bus. The man picked up the suitcase and followed the widow onto the bus. He set the briefcase down beside the woman and sat down behind her.

Then, the man began to think. "That suitcase was heavy! I bet she has something unbelievably valuable in it."

At the next bus stop, the man grabbed the suitcase beside the old widow and ran out of the bus's back door. He ran down the street with the luggage.

"Oh my!" exclaimed the widow lady. She was pleased. She had gotten rid of her dead dog, Rover. It had only cost her a bus fare and an old, worn-out suitcase. She chuckled to herself as she thought, "I wonder what that old man thought when he opened up the suitcase and discovered the treasure inside was only an old dead dog."

"Lay not up for yourselves treasures upon earth, where moth and rust doth corrupt, and where thieves break through and steal: But lay up for yourselves treasures in heaven, where neither moth nor rust doth corrupt, and where thieves do not break through nor steal: For where your treasure is, there will your heart be also."

- Matthew 6:19-21

THE WOMAN WAS VERY HAPPY!
SHE WENT BACK HOME.

THE END

CHAPTER TWO

AN UNEXPECTED CHRISTMAS DINNER GUEST

DUCKY DUCK ON HIS WAY TO "V" FLIGHT SCHOOL

SIGN UP TO FLY SOUTH

V FLIGHT SCHOOL

"FLY SOUTH FOR THE WINTER! ESCAPE THE COLD!"

Ducky Duck signed up for the trip south for the winter. It was going to be a very cold winter, and Ducky was not very industrious. Some might even say that Ducky Duck was lazy. So, when he heard that they were taking on passengers to fly south, he signed up.

The day arrived, and they made their assignments on the order in which they were to fly. As you may know, ducks fly together in a V-shape. That way, the wind and the wing movements from the ducks in front help make the traveling easier, especially for those behind the leader. Ducky found his place in the very back. The leader does most of the hard work. The other ducks are recipients of the efforts of those in front of them. Then they switch off, and the ones behind come up and take the lead. Ducky always managed to miss his turn at the front.

As the ducks were flying in their V-shaped form, they noticed a lovely pond down below. The leader circled, and they decided to take a break from their long trip south and stay a little while at this quiet, charming pond. They quickly noticed that this was not just any pond. It was part of a friendly, orderly farm. There were other farm animals close by: chickens, pigs, and cows.

WHILE FLYING SOUTH, THE FLOCK SAW A NICE FARM WITH A BARNYARD, ANIMALS, AND A BIG TROUGH OF FOOD.

FARMER JONES...

BARN

CHICKEN

SHEEP

COW

POND

...FEEDING THE ANIMALS IN THE BARNYARD

SO, THEY DECIDED TO STOP FOR THE NIGHT, TAKE A BREAK FROM THEIR TRIP, EAT AND REST.

While the ducks were taking their break, the farmer made his way down to the pen. Ducky quickly noticed that he was carrying food for the animals. Close by the pond was a small feeding trough for the pigs to eat. He also had a bucket full of grain that he scattered out for the chickens.

"Wow, what a luxury!" exclaimed Ducky Duck.

All the ducks ate to their hearts' content. They decided to rest for the night and leave at first light in the morning.

Ducky couldn't sleep that night. He thought of the long trip that was still ahead and all the

DUCKY ATE THE DELICIOUS FOOD. "WOW! IT IS SO GOOD!"

FOOD TROUGH

FARMER JONES

EVERYDAY, FARMER JONES CAME WITH A PAIL FULL OF FOOD.

DUCKY ATE AND ATE. HE WAS GOING TO FLY SOUTH WITH THE NEXT GROUP FLYING SOUTH,

BUT HE HAD PUT ON A LOT OF WEIGHT. NOW, HE WAS TOO FAT TO FLY! "I'LL DIET TOMORROW," THOUGHT DUCKY.

delicious food. Without a doubt, this was a five-star luxury hotel. He made a decision that night. "I am going to stay here for the winter," he thought to himself. "I will wait for my friends when they return next spring, and I will join them and go home."

The next day he said goodbye to his friends. They tried to tell Ducky that there were hidden problems for those barnyard chickens and animals, but Ducky had already made up his mind. He was not going to exhaust himself traveling so far when he could eat and enjoy life in luxury, or so he thought. Ducky would not listen to the reason of the other ducks or accept their advice. He knew that he would have an enjoyable vacation with a life of ease and plenty of food to eat, and he could lounge around in the pond all day.

Every day, Ducky Duck ate and enjoyed the delicious food. The farmer noticed this new addition to his barnyard animals. Although Ducky Duck was not one of his barnyard animals, the farmer made friends with Ducky Duck and gave him an extra helping of the grain. Ducky Duck did not notice that he was putting on excess weight. Because the food was so good and the farmer had been giving him extra, he became fatter and fatter.

Ducky also noticed that Farmer Jones had been humming and singing a catchy melody. He asked the other farm animals what the song was. They said, "It's Jingle Bells." Farmer Jones and his family always sang that song at this time of the season. However, usually one of our big fat hens disappears when we hear him humming and singing that melody."

The next day, Farmer Jones came out to feed the animals, but he was also holding an object that Ducky Duck had never seen before. It had a long handle and a striking shiny thing on the end. "Oh no! Run for your lives!" screamed the barnyard animals. "Farmer Jones has an ax in his hand." The barnyard animals scurried and ran everywhere in hiding. Ducky Duck had no idea why the other animals were so distracted. He had never seen an ax before. He knew nothing of the possible impending danger. Besides, Farmer Jones had the pail of food, and he was hungry.

The farmer laid the pail to one side. He picked up a long pole with a hook on the end. And then he started walking toward Ducky. He had a strange look in his eye that caused Ducky Duck to feel uncomfortable. And so Ducky began to run and was going to fly away from Farmer Jones, but he had overeaten and was so overweight that he couldn't fly. The long pole reached out, and as Ducky felt his webfoot being caught with the hook, he was pulled closer to Farmer Jones.

Farmer Jones grabbed Ducky by the legs and hung him upside down. And then he flung Ducky on the top of an old log. The last thing Ducky remembered was seeing the flashy something on the end of the handle called the ax, as it descended.

...And Ducky Duck became the uninvited Christmas guest.

When lust hath conceived, it bringeth forth sin: and sin, when it is finished, bringeth forth death. - James 1:15

There is a way which seemeth right unto a man, but the end thereof are the ways of death. -Proverbs 14:12

CHAPTER THREE

WALLY WALLOWER, THE PRODIGAL PIG

Wally Wallower was an industrious pig. He liked to think he was very smart. He had learned how to get to the feeding trough more quickly than all the other pigs in the pig pen. He enjoyed eating the slop that the farmer made for them from the leftovers of the table of the big white house on the hill. Wally Wallower watched every day as the farmer would come from the big white house on the hill to feed Wally Wallower and the other pigs in the pig pen.

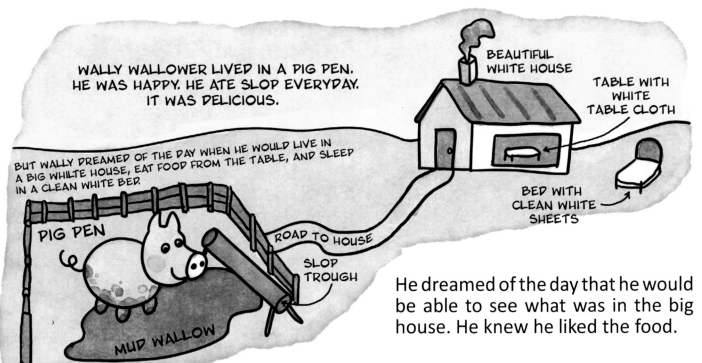

WALLY WALLOWER LIVED IN A PIG PEN. HE WAS HAPPY. HE ATE SLOP EVERYDAY. IT WAS DELICIOUS.

BEAUTIFUL WHITE HOUSE

TABLE WITH WHITE TABLE CLOTH

BUT WALLY DREAMED OF THE DAY WHEN HE WOULD LIVE IN A BIG WHILTE HOUSE, EAT FOOD FROM THE TABLE, AND SLEEP IN A CLEAN WHITE BED.

BED WITH CLEAN WHITE SHEETS

PIG PEN

ROAD TO HOUSE

SLOP TROUGH

MUD WALLOW

He dreamed of the day that he would be able to see what was in the big house. He knew he liked the food.

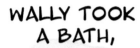

WALLY TOOK A BATH,

PUT ON A BOW TIE,

PUT ON A SUIT,

AND PUT ON COLOGNE.

WALLY THEN WENT TO LIVE AT THE WHITE HOUSE.

One day, Wally Wallower decided to take a bath and clean up spick-and-span. He put a nice colorful bowtie around his neck. He put some cologne under his arms so that he smelled great.

Off Wally Wallower marched up the hill to the big white house. He was so happy! That day, Wally Wallower ate at the table that had a big white tablecloth on top. The food was delicious and tasty, but the way Wally had to eat, it was almost impossible to enjoy the food. He had been so accustomed just to enjoy a delicious trough of slop. He had to eat with a knife and a fork.

FORK

KNIFE

DELICIOUS FOOD

TABLE CLOTH

THAT DAY, WALLY WALLOWER ATE AT THE TABLE WITH A WHITE TABLECLOTH.

HE THOUGHT
HE WAS IN
HOG HEAVEN!

FLUFFY
WHITE
PILLOWCASE

CLEAN
WHITE SHEETS

THAT NIGHT, WALLY
SLEPT IN A BED WITH
CLEAN WHITE SHEETS.

He couldn't just slop it down. He even had to put a nice white napkin in his lap.

That night, before he went to sleep, he had to take a bath. He soaked for a while in the bathtub until he was clean as a whistle. He got out of the bathtub, drying himself off with a white towel. He put on his clean pajamas and went to his bed. The bed was a wonderfully comfortable bed with white sheets covering the bed. So, Wally Wallower climbed into bed and pulled up the sheets to cover up. Then he nestled down to sleep.

Although the bed was unbelievably soft and comfortable, that night, Wally Wallower didn't sleep very well. He tossed and turned all night long. He dreamed of the good old days when he slept in the corner of the pig pen under the old dirty shed. He dreamed of eating the slop from the slop trough.

The next day Wally Wallower looked out of the window and down the hill. He saw the pig pen. He remembered his glory days in the pig pen, and he longed for it with precious memories. As the days dragged by, Wally Wallower became more and more disgruntled. He didn't

HAPPY PIG'S LIFE

BUT THEN WALLY REMEMBERED
THE GOOD OLD DAYS

WHEN HE ATE
DELICIOUS SLOP

AND WALLOWED IN
THE MUD.

like taking a bath every single day. He didn't like having to eat at a table with knives and forks, spoons, bowls, and plates.

So one day Wally Wallower decided to return to his pig pen. The moral of the story is you can take a pig out of a pigpen, but you cannot take the pig pen out of a pig.

"But it is happened unto them according to the true proverb, the dog is turned to his own vomit again; and the sow that was washed to her wallowing in the mire." - 2 Peter 2:22

SO, WALLY WALLOWER
RETURNED HOME.

THE PRODIGAL PIG LEFT HIS
FATHER AT THE PIG PEN AND
JOURNEYED TO THE BIG WHITE
HOUSE.

BUT THEN, HE REMEMBERED
HIS TRUE NATURE AND
RETURNED TO HIS REAL,
FORMER LIFE.

BACK
PACK

YOU CAN TAKE A PIG OUT
OF THE PIG PEN,
BUT YOU CAN'T TAKE
THE PIG PEN OUT OF THE PIG

TO PIG PEN

CHAPTER FOUR

WOLVES ARE JUST LIKE SHEEP

by James H. Gage (adapted from "The Sheep in Wolf's Clothing" by James Thurber)

There were once two cities, Sheepsville and Wolvesville. A mountain separated these two cities. Since wolves love to eat sheep, Sheepsville invested a lot of money to build a protective fence around their city. They also employed guards, which they posted at the gate of the town.

One day, the Sheepsville Times, a local newspaper, sent two sheep reporters to check Wolvesville. The two reporters went to the top of the mountain and hid behind a tree.

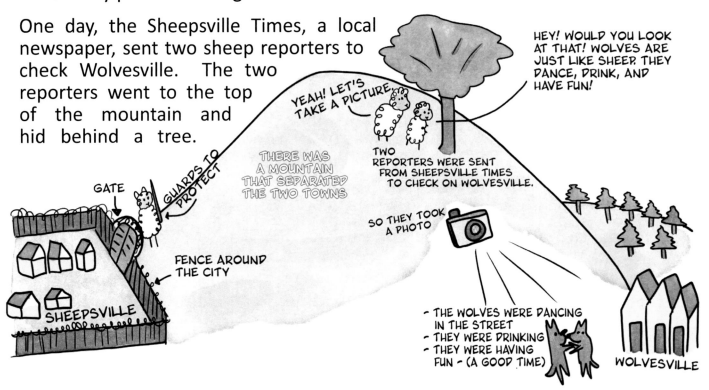

NEWSPAPER

They wanted to observe Wolvesville at a distance, and what they saw astounded them. They couldn't believe their eyes. The wolves were dancing in the streets and drinking lobo-cola, a local beverage. They were having fun and having a really good time. One of the sheep said, "Hey, would you look at that! Wolves are just like sheep. They dance, sing, and have fun just like us." "Yeah," said the other, "We'd better take some pictures."

Since the two reporters didn't bother to check further, little did the two reporters know why Wolvesville was so happy. The real reason Wolvesville was dancing, singing, and having a good time was that that very day, Miss Wolf from Wolvesville had just won the beauty pageant in the city of Cartagena. So, everyone was celebrating in honor of her victory.

After the reporters had taken some photos, they returned to Sheepsville and typed up their story. The next day, the headlines of the Newspaper read, "WOLVES ARE JUST LIKE SHEEP." Of course, everyone bought the paper. It was the noise of the town. Everyone was talking about how WOLVES ARE JUST LIKE SHEEP.

The City Council members read the same article and called a town meeting. "Wow! Look at this. Wolves are just like us," said one of the delegates. Another said, "Man are we ever dumb ... spending our hard-earned money on fences and guards." "We could save a lot of money if we took down the fences and fired the guards. After all, look at the photos and headlines in the newspaper, 'WOLVES ARE JUST LIKE SHEEP.'"

MISS WOLF HAD JUST WON THE BEAUTY PAGEANT IN CARTEGENA

EVERYONE BOUGHT THE NEWSPAPER

WOW! LOOK AT THIS! WOLVES ARE JUST LIKE US!

MAN ARE WE DUMB FOR SPENDING MONEY ON FENCES AND GUARDS!

CITY COUNCIL OF SHEEPSVILLE

THEY VOTED TO REMOVE THE FENCE AND LAY OFF THE GUARDS.

WE COULD SAVE A LOT IF WE TOOK DOWN THE FENCE AND FIRED THE GUARDS.

So, the city council voted to take down the fences. They laid off the guards. The whole city was so proud of the money they would save. "We'll probably get reelected after this," observed one of Sheepsville's City Council members.

A few days later, there was a full moon. One of the wolves went to the top of the mountain and howled. He looked down on Sheepsville. He rubbed his eyes in disbelief. "Could this be true? Is this happening?" he asked himself. Sure enough, there were no guards at the gate. There was no gate. Even better, there was no fence. So the wolf, after howling a bit, went back to Wolvesville to tell his friends.

That night, the night of the full moon, the wolves attacked Sheepsville and ate up all the sheep.

MORAL: Don't believe everything that you see. Don't believe everything that you read. Get the facts first, then decide.

I am the good shepherd: the good shepherd giveth his life for the sheep. But he that is an hireling, and not the shepherd, whose own the sheep are not, seeth the wolf coming, and leaveth the sheep, and fleeth: and the wolf catcheth them, and scattereth the sheep.

- John 10:11-12

CHAPTER FIVE

YOU CAN'T FOOL UNCLE SAM

There was a father who had written a letter. He put the letter into an envelope, but he discovered that he did not have a stamp. He called his son Peter and gave him a dollar to go to the post office and buy a postage stamp. He instructed Peter to put the postage stamp on the letter and then mail the letter.

Peter was anxious to obey his father. But Peter had a problem. He had never bought a stamp before. When he arrived at the post office, he hid behind a tree to watch and observe so that he could find out how to buy a stamp.

There were a lot of people standing in line. They went to a window, and behind the window, there was a clerk. The people gave money to the clerk, and the clerk gave the stamp to the people. The person then took the stamp, licked it, and put it on the letter. Then they took the letter to the mailbox and put the letter into the mailbox before leaving the post office.

Peter took his time observing. Then, he thought of a brilliant idea. He would make his dad proud of him. He would save a dollar and give it back to his dad. Here is what he did.

Peter waited until there was nobody around. Then he ran to the mailbox and dropped the letter into the mailbox where the slot was. He did not buy a stamp.

HE OBSERVED:

1. THE PEOPLE WENT TO THE WINDOW
2. THERE WAS A CLERK BEHIND THE WINDOW
3. THE PEOPLE GAVE THE CLERK MONEY
4. THE CLERK GAVE THE PEOPLE A STAMP
5. THEY PUT THE STAMP ON THE LETTER
6. THEY WENT TO THE MAILBOX
7. THEY PUT THE LETTER IN THE SLOT OF THE MAILBOX

SO HE GAVE HIS SON $1.00 HE SENT HIS SON TO THE POST OFFICE. "BUY A STAMP, PUT THE STAMP ON THE LETTER, AND MAIL THE LETTER."

TO THE POST OFFICE

PETER HID BEHIND A TREE, AND HE WATCHED.

FLAG

U.S. POST OFFICE

CLERK

SLOT

MAIL BOX

U.S. MAIL

PEOPLE WAITING IN LINE

He thought he had saved one dollar. He was so happy with himself. He just knew that his dad would be so delighted with him.

On the way home, Peter saw a sales vendor selling ice cream cones. Peter had one dollar, so he went to the vendor and asked how much it cost an ice cream cone. The man said it was 50 cents.

PETER HAD AN IDEA

HE SAID TO HIMSELF, "I'LL BE SMART. DAD WILL BE PROUD OF ME. I'LL SAVE $1.⁰⁰"

- HE WAITED UNTIL THERE WAS NOBODY AROUND
- THEN HE RAN TO THE MAILBOX
- HE PUT THE LETTER IN THE MAILBOX
- HE DIDN'T BUY A STAMP

"Wow, I can buy an ice cream cone and still give 50 cents back to dad," thought Peter to himself.

TO PETER'S HOUSE

ON THE WAY HOME HE BOUGHT AN ICE CREAM CONE.

PETER SPENT 50¢ CENTS FOR AN ICE CREAM CONE

When Peter arrived at the house, he was still eating the ice cream cone. He happily gave the 50 cents back to his dad.

"Peter, where did you get the ice cream cone, and why do I have 50 cents?" asked his father.

Of course, Peter very happily explained how he had mailed the letter. He had quickly gone to the mailbox when nobody was around and put the letter into the mailbox.

Peter's father had to take the time to instruct his son. You cannot fool Uncle Sam. It is necessary to buy a stamp because the letter will not be mailed if it does not have the proper postage stamp on it.

"Let him that is taught in the word communicate unto him that teacheth in all good things. Be not deceived; God is not mocked: for whatsoever a man soweth, that shall he also reap. - Galatians 6:6-7

WHEN PETER GOT BACK HOME, HE GAVE THE CHANGE (50¢) BACK TO HIS DAD.

"SON, WHERE DID YOU GET THIS MONEY?" ASKED THE FATHER.

SO PETER EXPLAINED HOW SMART HE HAD BEEN.

AND SO, DAD EXPAINED TO HIS SON PETER THAT YOU CAN'T FOOL UNCLE SAM.

CHAPTER SIX

THE WORLD'S BIGGEST FOOL

Paul was wealthy. It's okay to be rich, but in Paul's case, he was also a showoff. He liked to flash his money around.

Since Paul was rich, he bought one of the world's most expensive emeralds. It was beautiful. Then, he decided to take a trip around the world. He wanted to show off his newest possession, the emerald. So, he booked a cruise on a big ocean liner.

THIS IS ONE OF THE WORLD'S MOST EXPENSIVE EMERALDS

It cost a lot of money. But it was worth it, and remember, he was rich.

Onboard, Paul walked from person to person to show everyone his expensive emerald. He flashed it was he walked by to let everyone see it. Everybody said, "Ahh! What a beautiful emerald! That must have cost a lot of money."

However, soon the people lost interest and began to walk away.

To get their interest back, Paul began to throw the emerald up into the air. Everyone gathered around again. Someone said, "Wow!! Would you just look at that! How very dumb to risk something so precious!" But soon, the people lost their interest.

Paul then did something vastly different. He went to the side of the boat and began to toss the emerald up into the air. His hands were just over the side of the ship's rail. Just then, the ship leaned and tilted a little, and the emerald fell into the ocean. And everyone said, AHH!! HA, HA!!! THAT MAN IS SO DUMB! SURELY HE MUST BE THE WORLD'S BIGGEST FOOL."

"For what is a man profited, if he shall gain the whole world, and lose his own soul? or what shall a man give in exchange for his soul?"
                                        - Matthew 26:16

CHAPTER SEVEN

HOW TO CATCH PIGEONS

CALVIN COOLIDGE WAS THE PRESIDENT OF THE UNITED STATES.

HE TOLD THIS STORY ABOUT HIMSELF.

One of the United States' former presidents, Calvin Coolidge, once told this story about himself when he was a boy. He used to catch pigeons in his backyard, and here is the way that he captured them.

THE TRAP: He made a pigeon trap with a box. He would lift one end and then place a stick under it. Then he tied a string to the stick. Then he took some corn or rice and put it under the box. He held the string and hid behind a tree to wait. When the pigeons flew into the backyard and saw the corn or rice, they would fly under the box to eat. While the pigeons were under the box eating, Calvin pulled the string attached to the stick, and the box would fall over the top of the pigeons catching them.

TEN PIGEONS

BACKYARD

CALVIN WOULD HIDE BEHIND A TREE

A BOX WITH ONE END LIFTED UP (RAISED)

STRING TIED TO A STICK

CORN OR RICE UNDER THE BOX

THE STORY: One day, Calvin was in his backyard catching some pigeons. Ten pigeons flew into the backyard and landed on the fence. Immediately, nine of the pigeons flew under the box, but Calvin decided to wait for the last pigeon. However, while he waited, two of the nine pigeons flew out from under the trap. Now there were only seven pigeons left under the box. Calvin waited for the two pigeons to return and the other pigeon that was still on the fence. He wanted them too. Instead, two more pigeons flew away from under the box leaving only five. How could he be satisfied with only five when he could have had nine. So, he waited for the others to return, but they didn't return. One by one, the other pigeons left the box. Calvin caught no pigeons that day.

"And he said unto them, Take heed, and beware of covetousness: for a man's life consisteth not in the abundance of the things which he possesseth." - Luke 12:15

CHAPTER EIGHT

HOW TO GET RID OF YOUR ENEMIES

Once there lived a monkey and a lion in the forest. Every day the lion would come by and slap the monkey. The monkey was upset because he was so small and the lion so big and strong. The monkey decided to do something about it. He wanted to get even with the lion. He said to himself, "I'm going to show that big old bully the lion who's boss."

So, the monkey started working out and lifting weights. While the monkey was exercising, the elephant came by. "What are you doing?" asked the elephant. "I'm lifting weights. I'm going to get strong and beat up that old bully, the lion. Who does he think he is anyway?" said the monkey.

A MONKEY AND A LION LIVED IN A FOREST.

LION

MONKEY

OUCH!

SLAP!!

POW!
TAKE THAT!
I'M THE KING!

OUT OF MY WAY!

EVERYDAY, THE LION WOULD WALK BY THE MONKEY AND GIVE HIM A BIG SLAP!

Then the rabbit stopped and asked the monkey, "What are you doing?" "I'm working out and getting in shape to get even with that old bully, the lion. He thinks he is the king of the mountain. I'll show him!"

Later the turtle thought it was interesting to see a monkey lifting weights, so he decided to ask the monkey what he was doing. The monkey said, "I'm going to really take care of that big old bully, the lion, as soon as I get a little stronger."

SO THE MONKEY DECIDED TO GET EVEN. HE STARTED LIFTING WEIGHTS.

"WHAT ARE YOU DOING?" ASKED THE ELEPHANT.

I'M LIFTING WEIGHTS. I'M GOING TO GET STRONG AND BEAT UP THAT OLD BULLY LION!

"WHAT ARE YOU DOING?" ASKED THE RABBIT.

"WHAT ARE YOU DOING?" ASKED THE TURTLE.

Just then, the big old bully lion came by. He saw the monkey lifting weights and mumbling to himself. "Hey, dummy. What are you doing?"

"Well, to be frank, I'm lifting weights. I'm getting in shape so that I can beat it out of here really fast!"

*"As a roaring lion, and a ranging bear; so is a
wicked ruler over the poor people."
- Proverbs 28:15*

CHAPTER NINE

THE TASTY BIRD

(Told by Darlene McDaniel)

PETER LIVED IN CALIFORNIA

CALIFORNIA

COLOMBIA

TEXAS

PETER HAD BEEN WORKING IN COLOMBIA, BUT HE CALLED HIS MOM EVERY WEEK.

ONE WEEK, HE FORGET TO CALL HIS MOM WHO LIVED IN TEXAS.

Peter's mother lived in Texas. He was a son that really loved his mother. He had always taken care of her, especially since his father had passed away. He was a hard-working lad and had a good job. However, his career had moved him to Colombia, South America. He was far away from his mother.

He called her every week to tell her hello and let her know how much he loved her.

One week he forgot to call. He knew he was in trouble. Christmas was just around the corner, and this year, Peter was not going to be able to be with his mother at Christmas time.

He really wanted to do something special for his mother. Peter looked for an appropriate gift, one that he was sure his mother would enjoy.

He found an exotic bird at a pet shop. It was an intelligent parrot that spoke three languages. He was sure that his mother would really enjoy this gift. Besides, he had spent $500 on the bird and shipped the bird to his mom in Texas.

In a few days, he called his mom to see if she had received the present from him.

"Hi mom, how did you like the gift I sent. The parrot speaks three languages. It cost me a lot of money. I hope you really enjoy it."

"Well, son, I don't know anything about English, Spanish, or Italian. I'm sorry you spent a lot of money, but thank you for the gift! The bird really TASTED GREAT!" explained Peter's mom.

"But if any provide not for his own, and specially for those of his own house, he hath denied the faith, and is worse than an infidel." - 1 Timothy 5:8

CHAPTER TEN

FOUR BLIND MEN AND AN ELEPHANT

Four blind men sat every day in front of an enormous castle. Every morning a prince left the palace, riding an elephant. Although the blind men could not see the elephant, they knew that the animal had to be very large. "I wonder what an elephant looks like," said one of the blind man. "Me too," answered another.

"Why don't we ask the prince if he will let us feel the elephant?" said the third blind man. So, the fourth man asked the Prince if they could feel the elephant. Of course, the Prince said, "Sure, happy to oblige!"

One by one, each blind man felt the elephant. The first blind man felt the tail and said, "I know what an elephant looks like. An elephant looks like a rope." The second blind man felt the side and said, "I know what an elephant looks like. It looks like a wall. The third blind man felt the leg and said, "I know what an elephant looks like. An elephant looks like a tree." The fourth and last blind man felt the nose and said, "I know what an elephant looks like. It looks like a water hose."

AFTER THE PRINCE LEFT ON HS ELEPHANT, THE FOUR BLIND MEN BEGAN TO TALK ABOUT WHAT AN ELEPHANT LOOKED LIKE. THEY ARGUED ALL DAY LONG. WHICH ONE WAS CORRECT? DID ANY ONE OF THEM HAVE THE RIGHT ANSWER?

After the Prince left on his elephant, the four blind men began to talk about what an elephant looks like. They argued all day long. Can you tell which blind man was correct? Were any of them right? How could they have had a better understanding of what an elephant looks like?

"A wise man will hear, and will increase learning; and a man of understanding shall attain unto wise counsels."- Proverbs 1:5

CHAPTER ELEVEN

THE MICE COUNCIL

Adapted by James H. Gage Sr

There was a family of mice that lived in a hole in the wall of a house. They were a happy family, but they had a big problem. In the same place, there lived a big old bad cat. Every time one of the mice left his home in the wall to go to the kitchen to get something to eat, the big old bad cat would chase them.

THE MICE FAMILY LIVED IN A WALL.
THEY WERE HAPPY,
BUT THEY HAD A PROBLEM.

One day, White Whiskers, the President of the Mice Council, called a meeting to talk about the problem. "Fellow Mice," said White Whiskers after he had opened the council, "What are we going to do. We have a big problem. Every time we go to the kitchen to get some cheese or something to eat, that big old bad cat chases us. It's a matter of time until he catches one of us and eats us up."

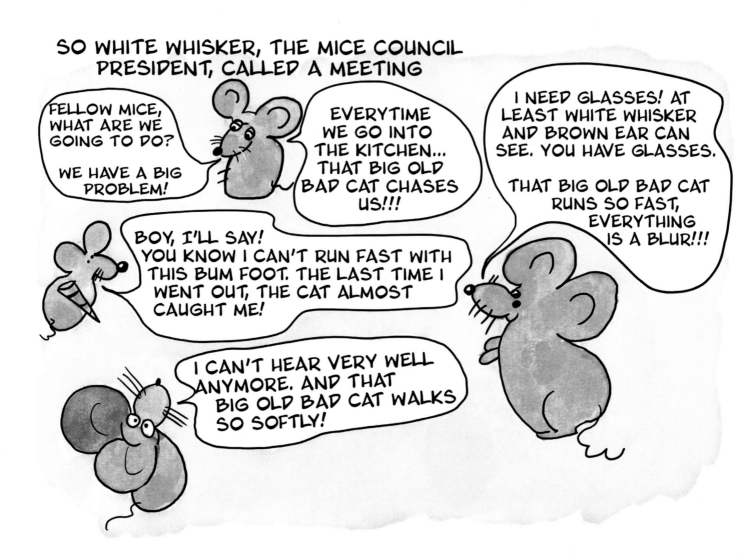

"Boy, I'll say," added Lousy Foot Debbie. "You know that I can't run fast with this bum foot of mine. The last time I went out, the cat almost caught me."

Brown Ear McGee said, "I can't hear very well anymore. And, that big old bad cat walks so softly. He just sneaks up on you before you know it."

False Teeth Charly said, "I need glasses! At least White Whisker, our President, and Brown Ear McGee have glasses and can see. That big old bad cat runs so fast that everything is a blur..."

Lousy Foot Debbie said, "You know, I've been thinking, and I have an idea. Why don't we put a bell around the cat's neck?" "Wow!!!" everyone shouted. "What a great idea."

"Okay, next order of business. If everyone agrees with Lousy Foot Debbie's idea, who will put the bell around that big old bad cat's neck?" said White Whiskers.

Indeed, everyone wanted to help. It was such a great idea, BUT ...

Lousy Food Debbie said, "I can't do it because I can't run fast." Brown Ear McGee said, "I can't do it either because I can't hear very well." False Teeth Charlie said, "Don't look at me. You know that I can't see well enough."

White Whisker said, "Well, I'm the President, and it's not my duty."

Every mouse had an excuse to not put the bell around the cat's neck. So the grand idea of the mice council failed. The mice still had a huge problem. Problems will never be solved if no one is willing to do something about it.

"Have I not commanded you? Be strong and courageous. Do not be afraid; do not be discouraged, for the Lord your God will be with you wherever you go."

- Joshua 1:9

A DIVISION OF:
BAPTIST TRAINING CENTER PUBLICATIONS

Made in the USA
Columbia, SC
24 August 2021